M000012926

Little American

_____
(child's name)

_____   _____
(age)   (date)

It is my hope that parents will use this book
as a tool to comfort and help children
understand what our Nation is experiencing.

Little Americans

is a result of questions my young children were asking.
It is intended as a guide to reassure young minds
that we are a freedom-loving Nation
with the ability to unite, overcome,
and gain strength through adversity -
as we have so many times in our past.

"I wish you love and peace," Lisa

Dedicated to every precious "Little American."
May you grow and prosper in a peaceful Nation.

"What is Patriotism and all of the flags I see?
I keep hearing the word 'America' and it is confusing me."

Our pledge explains Patriotism and why America is grand.
Americans say it together all across this great land.

" I promise to support
and defend.
If there is a need,
my help I will send."

"I pledge allegiance . . .

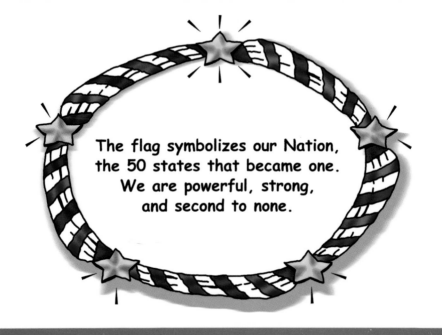

The flag symbolizes our Nation,
the 50 states that became one.
We are powerful, strong,
and second to none.

. . . to the flag of the United States of America . . .

Instead of having a king
to tell us what to do,
The choices are left
up to me and you.

. . . and to the Republic for which it stands . . .

God has blessed and protected
America from the start;
No one or nothing
can break it apart.

. . . One Nation under God, Indivisible . . .

We have the ability
to make our own choices
and the power to be free.
Everyone is treated
fairly and equally.

. . . With Liberty and Justice for all."

We realize that our freedom and security are precious and glorious.
ur Country has faced struggles before yet always remained victorious.

To have a peaceful Nation, we all must do our part,
For within you and me is where peace must start.

So remember when you see the American flag wave,
We live in the land of the free and the home of the brave.

I pledge allegiance to the flag,
of the United States of America
and to the Republic
for which it stands
one Nation under God,
Indivisible
with Liberty and Justice
for all.